ROCK 'N LEARN®

Phonics
Volumes I & II

written and produced by:
Brad Caudle
Richard Caudle

vocals by:
Tom McCain
Shawn Dady
Susan Elliot
Brad Caudle

voices:
Eric Leikam,
Susan Rand
Mick Perry

rap performances:
Robert Witherspoon
Richard Caudle

inside illustrations:
Bart Harlan

Instructional Guide

What do learners need to know before using Rock 'N Learn Phonics?

Learners should be able to recognize capital and lowercase letters. (*Rock 'N Learn Alphabet* audio or video programs can help develop these skills.) Because line numbers are used for keeping place, learners should be able to recognize numerals 1 through 10. (*Rock 'N Learn Colors, Shapes & Counting* audio or video programs teach number recognition.) You may also need to teach students the left-to-right direction for reading.

How can I assist the student?

While students are learning to read, they can also develop spelling skills by writing words from the program as you dictate them. Eventually, assist students in writing short sentences.

Rock 'N Learn produces *Phonics Easy Readers on DVD*, with brightly illustrated stories that correspond to each section of the audio program and build in complexity. A librarian may help in locating other interesting reading material at an appropriate level.

Why are vowels introduced before consonants in this program?

Rock 'N Learn Phonics teaches students short vowels first because they are easy to learn and most consonants cannot be sounded properly without a vowel. The second song in this program combines vowels with consonants so that learners immediately start integrating them as one sound. Later in the program, we cover long vowels.

How long should learning sessions be?

We recommend only one or two songs per session along with a few of the preceding songs (for review). Learners should not go to *Volume II* until they can read all of the words on *Volume I* before the voice. Repeated exposure is the key to making this program work.

Where can students get more practice with the basic sounds of vowels and consonants?

We suggest *Rock 'N Learn Letter Sounds*, either in audio or video format. To locate a retailer near you, call 800-348-8445 or 936-539-2731. Visit us at *www.rocknlearn.com*.

Order of Presentation (followed by page number in book)

Volume I

1	Short Vowel Sounds	1
2	Beginning Consonants	2, 3
3	Practice with Beginning Consonants	2, 3
4	Special Sounds of *c, g, qu, x*	4, 5
5	Consonant-Vowel-Consonant Words	6
6	Words Ending in *ll, ss, ff*	6
7	Plural *s* and Ending *s*	7
8	Ending Consonant Blends: *ft, lf, lm, lp, lt, mp, nd, nk, nt, pt, sk, st*	7
9	Practice with Ending Consonant Blends	8
10	Beginning Consonant Blends: *bl, br, cl, cr, dr, fl, fr, gl, gr, pl, pr, sc, sk, sl, sm, sn, sp, st, sw, tr, tw*	9
11	Three-Letter Blends: *scr, spl, str*	9
12	Consonant Digraphs and Trigraphs: *ch, tch, ck, sh, th, wh, shr, squ, thr*	10
13	Silent *e* Introduction	11
14	Silent *e* Makes the Long Vowel Sound	11
15	Silent *e* Practice	12
16	Fun Quiz	13

Volume II

1	Introduction to Long *a*	14
2	Practice with Long *a (ai, ay)*	14
3	Introduction to Long *e*	14
4	Practice with Long *e (ee, ea,* introduction to homonyms, *e, ie)*	14
5	Introduction to Long *i*	15
6	Practice with Long *i (ie, y, ind)*	15
7	Introduction to Long *o*	15
8	Practice with Long *o (oa, oe, ol, ow, o)*	15
9	Introduction to Long *u* and *oo*	16
10	Practice with Long *u* and *oo (ew, ou, ui, ue, oo, o)*	16
11	*r*-Controlled Vowel: *ar*	17
12	*r*-Controlled Vowels: *er, ir, ur*	17
13	*r*-Controlled Vowel: *or*	17
14	*r*-Controlled Vowels: *ire, are, air*	17
15	Diphthongs: *oi, oy, ou, ow*	18
16	*au, aw, all, al*	18
17	Break It Down (Syllables) & The Schwa Sound	19
18	Ending Sounds: *ing, ink, ank, ang, ong, ung, dge*	19
19	Ending Sounds: *y, le*	20
20	Rule Breakers	20
21	*ph* and *gh*	21
22	Common Sight Words	21
23	Silent Consonants: *c, k, w, gh, g, b*	22
24	Bonus Instrumental Track	

A E I O U (Y)

Aa

apple

Ee

egg

I i

igloo

Oo

ostrich

Uu

up

Bb	**ba**t		**bi**g	**bu**g
Dd	**do**g		**di**d	**da**d
Ff	**fa**n		**fi**n	**fu**n
Hh	**ha**t		**ho**t	**hi**m
Jj	**je**t		**jo**t	**ja**m
Kk	**ki**d		**ki**t	**ki**n
Ll	**li**p		**la**p	**le**t
Mm	**ma**n		**me**t	**mo**p

Nn	**ne**t		**nu**t	**no**t
Pp	**pi**g		**pe**t	**pu**p
Rr	**ra**t		**re**d	**ru**n
Ss	**su**n		**si**t	**sa**t
Tt	**te**n		**ta**n	**ti**p
Vv	**va**n		**ve**t	**va**t
Ww	**we**b		**wi**t	**we**t
Yy	**ya**k		**ye**t	**yu**m
Zz	**zi**p		**zi**g	**za**g

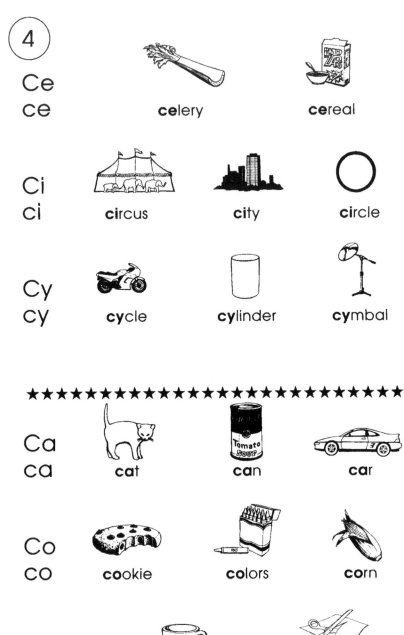

4

Ce
ce — **ce**lery **ce**real

Ci
ci — **ci**rcus **ci**ty **ci**rcle

Cy
cy — **cy**cle **cy**linder **cy**mbal

★★★★★★★★★★★★★★★★★★★★★★★★

Ca
ca — **ca**t **ca**n **ca**r

Co
co — **co**okie **co**lors **co**rn

Cu
cu — **cu**p **cu**t

Gg

girl   gold   guitar

Gg

gem   giant   giraffe

★★★★★★★★★★★★★★★★★★★★★★★★★★★

Qu

qu

queen   question   quarter   quiet

★★★★★★★★★★★★★★★★★★★★★★★★★★★

Xx

xylophone   box

1. at	mat	set	get
2. it	hit	quit	fit
3. mix	six	ox	fox
4. in	win	beg	leg
5. job	rob	jut	but
6. bag	rag	top	pop
7. nap	map	rub	tub
8. men	pen	dot	got
9. an	ran	pan	ban
10. had	mad	sad	bad

★★★★★★★★★★★★★★★★★★★★★★★★★★★★★

1. mess	miss	pass	kiss
2. tell	well	sell	bell
3. will	hill	pill	fill
4. puff	muff	cuff	buff

cat    cats

can   cans

dog   dogs

1. lips   hats   caps   bats

2. pans   bugs   hills   pens

3. bus   as   has

4. is   his   yes

1. milk   

2. left   self   elm   help

3. belt   jump   and   honk

4. went   kept   ask   best

1. silk	elk	raft	soft
2. elf	golf	gulp	felt
3. melt	tilt	quilt	damp
4. camp	lamp	bump	limp
5. hand	land	end	bend
6. send	sunk	punk	bunk
7. tent	sent	hint	ant
8. pants	runt	wept	desk
9. disk	risk	mask	tusk
10. fast	rest	list	must

1. **bl**ess   **br**at   **cl**ub   **cr**ab

2. **dr**um   **fl**ag   **fr**og   **gl**ass

3. **gr**ass   **pl**um   **pr**om   **sc**ab

4. **sk**in   **sl**ip   **sm**og

5. **sn**ap   **sp**in   **st**op   **sw**im

6. **tr**ip   **tw**in

7. **scr**ub   **spl**it   **spr**int   **str**um

1. **ch**in   much   chill   chimp

2. fe**tch**   stretch   witch   scratch

3. ra**ck**   black   kick   rock

4. **sh**op   wish   dish   hush

5. **th**in   thump   with   bath

6. **th**is   that   then   them

7. **wh**en   which   whack   wham

8. **shr**imp   shred

9. **squ**ish   squid

10. **thr**ift   thrill

1. at→at**e**   can→can**e**   cap→cap**e**

2. cub→cube   cut→cute   bit→bite

3. dim→dime   fad→fade   hid→hide

4. hop→hope   kit→kite   mad→made

5. not→note   pan→pane   pet→Pete

6. pin→pine   plan→plane   rid→ride

7. rip→ripe   rob→robe   slid→slide

8. tap→tape   tot→tote   tub→tube

1. take   bake   snake   make   flute

2. face   race   these   those   nose

3. came   game   same   name   home

4. gate   late   skate   gave   five

5. joke   time   shine   fine   nine

6. size   prize   while   white   quite

7. hike   bike   like   ape   grape

8. ice   rice   use   nice   mice

9. age   cage   page   huge   strange

1. quiz   wig   off   pat   hut

2. fog   dug   clock   hop   am

3. if   on   crash   smell   rope

4. cost   drop   block   shelf   truck

5. trick   duck   still   tune   plate

6. place   brush   brick   shake   shrill

7. flame   splash   bed   sled   plant

8. glad   trap   twig   twice   its

9. blame   strip   struck   scrap   scrape

10. skunk   luck   quack   from   stamp

14

1. **p**a**i**d wait grain rain

2. mail snail chain train

3. **p**a**y** way ray

4. say day play may

★★★★★★★★★★★★★★★★★★★★★★★★★★★

1. **b**ee**p** sleep sheep bee

2. deep keep creep seed green

3. m**ea**l leak seat heat

4. read beak neat team

5. clean beach eat peace please

6. meet meat feet feat

7. see sea flee flea

8. b**e** he me she we

9. f**ie**ld shield thief piece chief

15

1. **pie**   tie   dried   lie

2. wh**y**   my   cry   fly   try   by

3. m**ind**   kind   find   blind   wind

★★★★★★★★★★★★★★★★★★★★★★★★★★★★★

1. **boa**t   goat   coat   road

2. soap   soak   roast   goal   float

3. **toe**   hoe   goes

4. **ol**d   hold   cold   sold   told   gold

5. bold   mold   fold   bolt   colt

6. sh**ow**   row   bow   mow

7. low   bowl   grow   snow   blow

8. g**o**   so   no

1. n**ew**　　　grew　　　stew　　　few

2. y**ou**　　　soup　　　group

3. fr**ui**t　　　suit　　　juice

4. bl**ue**　　　true　　　glue　　　clue

5. flew　　　　flu　　

6. f**oo**d　　　boo　　　mood　　　zoo

7. cool　　　tool　　　fool　　　pool

8. d**o**　　　to

(17)

1. **c**ar   far   jar   star   dark   bark

2. sharp   harp   hard   card   barn

3. art   smart   start   part   march

4. h**er**   perk   perch   fern   herd

5. sh**ir**t   dirt   bird   stir   first   third

6. f**ur**   curl   turn   burn   hurt

7. blur   purse   curve   burp

8. f**or**   porch   corn   or   horn

9. fort   sort   short   sports   born   cord

10. more

★★★★★★★★★★★★★★★★★★★★★★★★★★★★★★★

1. **tire**   hire   wire   fire

2. sh**are**   bare   care   scare   spare

are

3. **air**   pair   fair   hair

1. **boil**   oil   oink   point   coin

2. **boy**   joy   toy

3. **hou**se   mouse   out   trout   count

4. south   found   round   our   sour

5. c**ow**   now   plow   how

6. down   brown   owl   crowd

★★★★★★★★★★★★★★★★★★★★★★★★★★★★

1. **lau**nch   fault   cause   haul

2. dr**aw**   raw   straw   saw   paw

3. **all**   hall   ball   call   fall

4. **tal**k   stalk   walk   salt

(19)

1. person   into   between

2. water   backyard   maybe

3. bedroom   before   remember

4. sunshine   never   upon

5. until   because   myself

6. open   seven

7. **a**bout   away   around   amaze

★★★★★★★★★★★★★★★★★★★★★★★★

1. **sing**   ring   thing   bring   swing

2. **ink**   think   stink   shrink   drink

3. th**ank**   sank   blank   drank   bank

4. b**ang**   hang   sang   rang   twang

5. str**ong**   long   song   gong   belong

6. r**ung**   stung   lung   flung   hung

7. ba**dge**   fudge   bridge   judge   hedge

1. la**dy**   rainy   tiny   shiny

2. candy   easy   many   any

3. nutty   hobby   puppy   sunny

4. bunny   muddy   foggy   happy

5. piggy   penny   funny   pretty

6. mid**dle**   purple   stumble   little

7. tumble   turtle   crumble   bubble

★★★★★★★★★★★★★★★★★★★★★★★★★★★★★★

1. steak   break   great

2. bread   thread   head

3. sweat   read   said

4. would   could   should

5. touch   famous

6. shoulder   boulder

7. your   pour   four

8. wood   look   book   roof   good

1. **ph**oto   lau**gh**   phone   cough

2. trophy   tough   enough   elephant

★★★★★★★★★★★★★★★★★★★★★★★★★★★★★★

1. shoe most woman was done been

2. again both shall carry come of

3. only the does warm work give

4. have who once one wash want

5. some own put where women they

1. **sc**ent   scissors   scene

2. **k**now   knot   knee   knew   knock

3. **w**rong   wrist   wreck   wrap   write

4. ri**gh**t   fight   might   flight

5. tight   night   bright   sight

6. sigh   light   high   straight

7. eight   sleigh   weigh   neighbor

8. bought   fought   sought   caught

9. si**g**n   com**b**   thumb   lamb

Alphabet
Alphabet Al leads students on an exciting adventure with cool songs for each letter and musical games to reinforce letter/sound associations. DVD includes how to print capital and lowercase letters and numbers 0 through 9. Ages 2–5. Approx. 35 minutes.
RL945 DVD
RL957 Audio CD & Book

Alphabet Exercise
Alphabet Al promotes fitness and imaginative play while teaching children about letters. Young learners enjoy performing new and traditional exercises, developed with a certified fitness trainer. Ages 2–5. Approx. 37 minutes.
RL913 DVD

Alphabet Circus
Alphabet Al takes children to the circus where dancing dogs, crazy clowns, and amazing acrobats add excitement. Children learn words that begin with each letter. Ages 2–5. Approx. 35 minutes.
RL942 DVD

Colors, Shapes & Counting
Preschoolers join Rollie Roundman and friends to learn counting and sorting objects by color, shape, or a combination of both. Includes advanced concepts. Ages 2–5. Approx. 48 minutes.
RL944 DVD
RL932 Audio CD & Book

Dance With the Animals
Live footage of animals captivate children as they learn fun facts about animals, how to care for pets, and following directions. Ages 2–5. Approx. 45 minutes.
RL902 DVD

Nursery Rhymes
Brother and Sister Goose join Mother Goose to lead young learners through 43 rhymes, teaching them about safety, manners, and accepting responsibility. Ages 2–5. Approx. 40 minutes.
RL982 DVD
RL953 Audio CD & Book

Getting Ready for Kindergarten
Jill and Joey help preschoolers learn colors, counting, tying shoes, following directions, holding a pencil, printing letters and numbers, listening, and more. Ages 3–5. Approx. 45 minutes.
RL952 DVD

Math

Rock 'N Learn Math Rap, Rock & Country
Each set of facts has it's own cool song. Audio titles include a CD and book with reproducible lyrics. DVDs use energetic performers and colorful animation to hold attention. High interest for learners of all abilities. Download free puzzles, worksheets and games from www.worksheets-for-math.com. Addition and subtraction facts up to 18. Multiplication covers facts up to 12. Division divisors up to 9.

	AUDIO	DVD
Addition & Subtraction Rock	RL906	RL924
Addition & Subtraction Rap	RL918	RL923
Addition & Subtraction Country	RL933	
Multiplication Rap	RL907	RL921
Multiplication Rock	RL905	RL922
Multiplication Country	RL925	
Division Rap	RL908	RL980
Division Rock	RL941	

Telling Time
Timothy Time and friends teach students how to tell time to the hour and minute using a traditional analog clock. Students also learn days of the week, months of the year, counting by fives, and more. Ages 6 & up. Approx. 40 min.
RL947 DVD

Money & Making Change
The comical characters Penny and Bill help students learn strategies for counting coins and bills, "skip counting," expressing money in written terms, making change, and more. Ages 6 & up. Approx. 57 minutes.
RL928 DVD

Math Word Problems
Students learn how to read problems carefully, identify relevant information, use pictures and diagrams, and look for patterns. This is a great review of 3rd grade math. Grades 3-4. Approx. 58 min.
RL201 DVD

Beginning Fractions & Decimals
Learn rules about congruent parts, equivalent fractions, proper and improper fractions, mixed numerals, and more. Ages 8 & up.
RL981 DVD

Language Arts

Letter Sounds
Covers the most common sound that each letter makes. The on-screen mouth in DVD versions shows how to form each sound. By the end of this program, students are combining letters to read words and sentences. Ages 4–7. Approx. 55 minutes.
RL946 DVD
RL911 Audio CD & Book

Phonics, Vols. I & II
Includes vowels, consonants, blends, digraphs, "rule breakers," and more. Lively characters and humor introduce phonetic rules and provide plenty of practice reading words. The on-screen mouth helps learners check pronunciation. Ages 6 & up. Approx. 92 minutes.
RL948 DVD
RL901 Audio CD & Book

Phonics Easy Readers on DVD
Use with our Phonics programs to practice reading stories that progress from simple to complex.
RL954 DVD

Read Along Stories on DVD
Classic tales help build reading comprehension skills. Students work at their own pace with literature-based material at an approximate 2nd grade level. Ages 6 & up.
RL977 DVD

Reading Comprehension
Students learn to read for meaning and prepare for tests. With Marko's guidance, students ace a practice test by learning how to read passages, find key words, and determine the best answers. Grades 2–4.
Approx. 46 min.
RL200   DVD

Grammar
Students practice identifying nouns, verbs, linking verbs, verb tense, proper nouns, pronouns, and more.
35-minute audio CD. Ages 8 & up.
RL929 CD & BOOK

Writing Strategies
Boost skills by creating a hook, using transitional phrases and dialogue, applying colorful words, and mastering other tools such as personification.
Grades 4–12. Approx. 70 minutes.
RL202 DVD

Science

Physical Science
Covers lab safety, scientific method, atoms and their parts, molecules, states of matter, physical and chemical changes, mixtures versus pure substances, electricity, magnetism, motion, gravity, light, and energy. Grades 5 & up. Approx. 55 min.
RL204 DVD

Earth Science
Learn about the Solar System, weather, the water cycle, geology, properties of minerals, volcanoes, plate tectonics, weathering, topography, erosion, energy resources, and energy conservation. An excellent tool to prepare for any earth science test. Grades 5 & up. Approx. 58 min.
RL205 DVD

Life Science
Learn parts of a plant, photosynthesis, life cycles, genetic traits and adaptations, plant and animal cells, food webs, and more. Enjoy a surprise guest appearance by rock star Rubbert Plant. Grades 5 & up. Approx. 59 minutes.
RL206   DVD

Human Body
Explore the systems of the human body and the five senses. Take an exciting "amusement park" ride through the alimentary canal to learn about digestion. Grades 5 & up.
RL207 DVD

Solar System
Students join in with entertaining songs to learn the order of the planets and fun facts including size of planets, their atmosphere, moons, distance from the sun and more. Includes full-color book with photos from NASA. Ages 8 & up. Approx. 40 minutes.
RL960 Audio CD & Book

Dinosaur Rap
Learn amazing facts about carnivores, herbivores, and omnivores from prehistoric times. Covers over 40 dinosaurs, fossils, theories of extinction, and more. Includes full-color book with illustrations and lyrics. Ages 8 & up. Approx. 35 minutes.
RL959 Audio CD & Book